John Thompson's Modern Course
for the Piano

The
FIRST GRADE BOOK
Something New Every Lesson

Verses by Katherine Faith

A clear, correct and complete foundation in the study of the piano to enable the student to think and feel musically

WILLIS MUSIC

THE WILLIS MUSIC COMPANY

Exclusive Distributors:
Music Sales Limited
Newmarket Road, Bury St Edmunds, Suffolk IP33 3YB, UK.
Music Sales Pty Limited
20 Resolution Drive, Caringbah, NSW 2229, Australia.

Order No. WMR101090
ISBN: 978-1-84938-884-9

Engravings by Paul Ewers Music Design.
Edited by Toby Knowles.
CD mastered by Jonas Persson.

Printed in the EU.

CONTENTS

'Something New Every Lesson'

PREFACE

This book is designed for the use of beginner piano students. Perhaps the greatest recommendation for its use is that it 'makes haste slowly'. Many bad habits which hamper students in the upper grades are to be traced directly to faulty training in the beginning. Thus, many hours of labour and much financial outlay is incurred annually in the sometimes hopeless task of attempting to correct attitudes, habits, and mistakes that should never have been allowed to take root in the first place. 'As the twig is bent, the tree's inclined'; this old aphorism applies equally to muscular control, technique, time problems, musical conception, habits of thought and practice.

MAKE A SHOWING WITH STUDENTS

It is reasonable to assume that most errors are due less to inattention on the part of the teacher than to an eagerness to see the student progress rapidly. Sometimes they may be the fruit of using wrong material. A great many early-grade books have apparently been written for the exclusive use of 'budding geniuses', of whom there are all too few. Yet, even these would benefit immeasurably from a sounder method of learning fundamentals which, in a final analysis, have to be mastered anyway in the end at a great sacrifice of time and energy. The student who thoroughly masters every simple step as it presents itself and learns to play their little compositions cleanly, correctly and up-to-speed will make a far better showing than the one who is allowed to stumble in desultory fashion through more technically advanced music.

THIS IS A BEGINNER'S BOOK

Most of the pieces contained in this book are written in five-finger position. Towards the end there are a few examples of one-finger extensions. The book is for students of any age and it is assumed that the student has had some preliminary piano tuition at a preparatory level.

OBJECTIVES

The purpose of this book is to lay a clear, correct and complete foundation for piano study so that the student can think and feel musically. It is quite possible to teach beginner students how to play with musical understanding. Though they play simple melodies and very modest little pianistic patterns, they should be impressed with the fact that these are the bricks, as it were, which, when laid together, build the greatest compositions. If they learn to recognise and perform these small fragments properly and with intelligence, they will, as they progress, meet the larger forms of composition with perfect understanding, and will not be bewildered at the weaving together of many musical fragments into a perfect whole.

THE IMPORTANCE OF PATTERNS

With this in mind, the author lays much stress in this book on melody patterns, rhythmical patterns, harmony patterns and finger patterns. Any elementary student who learns to recognise patterns is a better sight-reader, memoriser, interpreter and, through a knowledge of finger patterns, a better pianist than the student who laboriously learns their compositions note-by-note. A note-by-note conception of music is not only antiquated, but apt to lessen interest and hinder progress. Do not allow students to acquire this habit if you wish to keep them interested.

FIVE-FINGER POSITIONS

Practically all of the examples in this book remain in the five-finger position. For this reason transposition is quite easy by means of finger patterns, and the student is given opportunity through actual experience to develop a real finger sense in five-finger groups before venturing into more complicated fingering. The five-finger group is the basis for scale and arpeggio fingering which follows later. Scales and arpeggios, of course, are the foundation of all piano technique: therefore five-finger drills should not be passed over in a superficial manner.

VARIATIONS ON FIVE-FINGER GROUPS

As students become familiar with several five-finger positions (C Major, F Major, G Major, etc.) they are, in this book, gradually introduced to examples combining more than one five-finger group. In other words, they learn that it is no more difficult to change from one five-finger position to another in the same piece than it is to do so in two pieces – each one of which requires a different position.

Students are also taught to recognise five-finger groups with extensions, that is, with one note added on either side of the group.

These simple extensions can be played without shifting the hands out of position. Such extensions also make it possible to enrich both the melodic and harmonic content of the little examples which ordinarily grow very monotonous when kept strictly within the five-note limit for the entire content of a book.

KEYBOARD ATTACKS

Since the piano is, after all, a mechanical instrument made up of keys, strings, hammers and other mundane materials, all our thoughts and emotions must be produced through it by the mechanical action of these mediums in direct communication with our fingers. The proper touch must be acquired or, regardless of the emotions of the performer, the piano will not respond. Therefore, the same keyboard attacks used by the great artists should be taught in miniature to the beginner.

Resolve that your students are to have the benefit of such training now. In perusing this book you will find that the following touches are definitely stressed: finger *legato*, phrasing attack, wrist *staccato*, forearm *legato* and *staccato*. If properly and carefully applied they will enable beginners to play little pieces with precision, expression and musical understanding. When they have finished the book, students will be ready and eager for their next step up the musical ladder onto the second grade book. They will have learned to play the piano as a musical instrument and not as a sort of typewriter.

John Thompson

P. S. Certificates of Merit have been included on page 79 as awards for 'Examination Reviews' on pages 20, 39, 57 and 75. – J. T.

HAND POSITION – C MAJOR

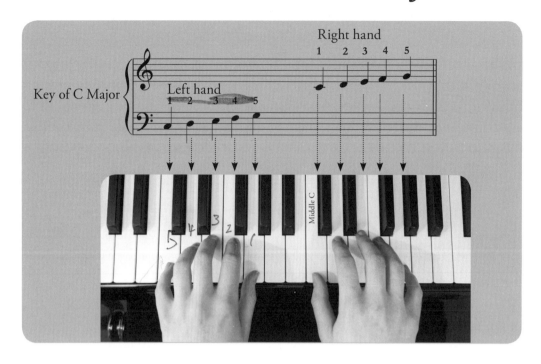

Before beginning to play this piece, place the hands in the position shown above. Play each hand separately a few times to get the feel of the five-finger position in the key of C Major.

MUSIC LAND

Track No. 1

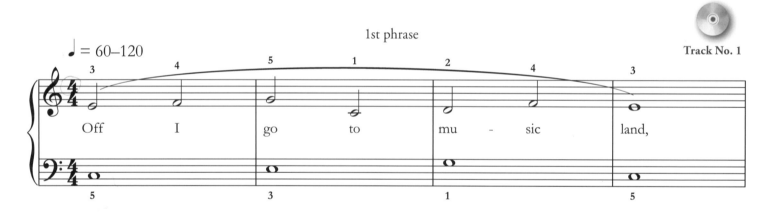

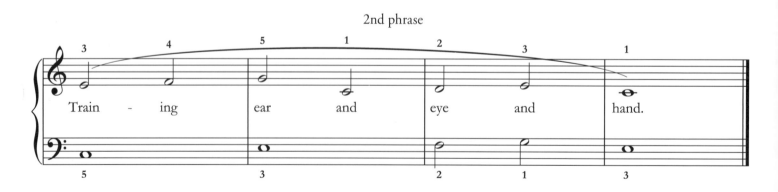

THE PHRASE

Music is a language. It can express thoughts and even tell stories – musical stories. When we hear a story we listen sentence by sentence, not letter by letter. So it is with music. Single notes by themselves mean nothing. Only when the notes are arranged into musical sentences do they take on a definite meaning. Musical sentences are called phrases. Learn to think of your music phrase by phrase. Note how the little musical story above is told in two phrases.

PATTERNS

(Use the same hand position as page opposite)

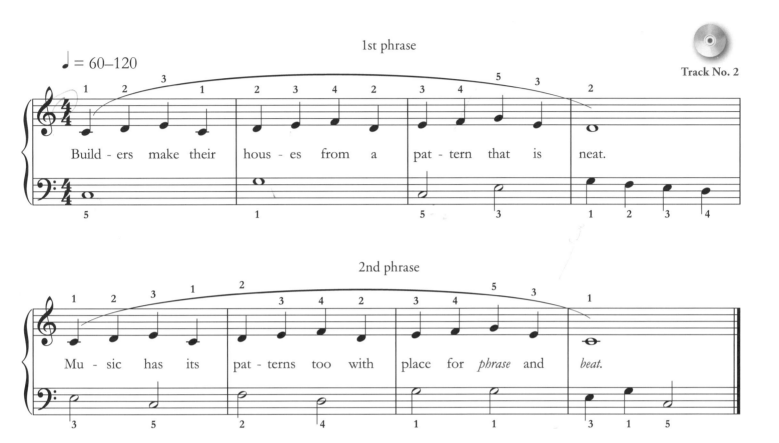

Track No. 2

♩ = 60–120

1st phrase

Build - ers make their hous - es from a pat - tern that is neat.

2nd phrase

Mu - sic has its pat - terns too with place for *phrase* and *beat.*

MUSICAL FORM

Because it is built up of many well-ordered patterns, music has often been compared to architecture. We have in music melody patterns, rhythmical patterns, harmony patterns and (in piano music) finger patterns. The ability to recognise patterns is very important. It makes for easier sight-reading, quicker memorising and more intelligent interpretation.

THE MELODY PATTERN

 Fix in your mind the melody pattern shown here in the right hand and note that the notes move three steps upward and one skip downward.

Note now that this design is repeated over and over throughout the little composition.
Each design starts one note higher than the preceding pattern.

The same pattern one white key higher.   The same pattern another white key higher.

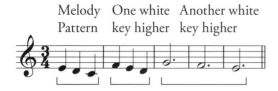

Practise C Major hand position as in previous pieces.

RUNAWAY RIVER

Track No. 3

At faster tempos it will be easier to count one-in-a-bar, up to ♩ = 50.

RHYTHM AND ACCENTS

Rhythm has been called the 'soul' of music. Rhythmical 'swing' gives life to any composition. The first step in setting the rhythm is by means of the accent. An accent is a special emphasis placed upon one of the beats in a bar. 'Runaway River' is written in ¾ time, which means that each crotchet lasts for one count, and there are three counts to a bar. Always accent the first beat of each bar in ¾ time. COUNT: | **ONE** two three | **ONE** two three | etc.

A $\frac{2}{4}$ time signature means one count to each crotchet and two counts to each bar.

Accent the first note of each bar. COUNT: | **ONE** two | **ONE** two | etc. Use the C Major hand position.

Hunt for the melody patterns. Think of your pieces phrase by phrase.

THE TRAFFIC COP

Track No. 4

TEMPO

Tempo means time. A steady, even tempo is necessary to preserve the rhythmical swing. This means that there is no time to stop and hunt for notes or fingers. After a piece has been learned, it should be reviewed until it can be played fluently and easily without stops or hesitation.

TONAL SHADING

As a painter creates beautiful pictures by lights and shadows, so do we add colour to our musical pictures by means of tonal shading. A melody line should constantly change in 'thickness'. This may be accomplished by adding more or less intensity to the tone. Everything possible should be done to make our music 'flow'. This applies equally to melody, rhythm and harmony. 'Contrast is the first law of all art.'

SWANS ON THE LAKE

Track No. 5

At faster tempos, it will be easier to count one-in-a-bar, up to ♩ = 50.

THE MEANING OF THE EXPRESSION MARKS USED IN THIS PIECE

Read carefully:

1) *Moderato.* At a moderate rate of speed or tempo.

2) *Legato.* Bound together, play smoothly and connected.

3) *mf* = *Mezzo forte.* Half or moderately loud.

4) *p* = *Piano.* Softly.

5) *f* = *Forte.* Loud.

6) *pp* = *Pianissimo.* Very Soft.

7) *mp* = *Mezzo piano.* Half or moderately soft.

8) Rit. = *Ritardando.* Gradual slowing up of tempo.

SEMITONES

A semitone is the distance between any key and the next nearest key to it.

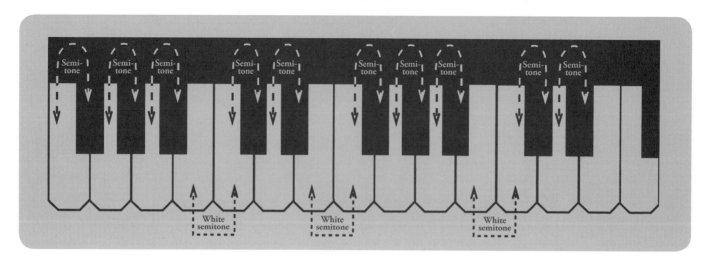

We find most of the semitones are from a white to a black key. There are, however, two white semitones – one between B and C and the other between E and F. Study them on this chart and locate them on the keyboard of your piano until you can quickly recognise them.

SHARPS AND FLATS

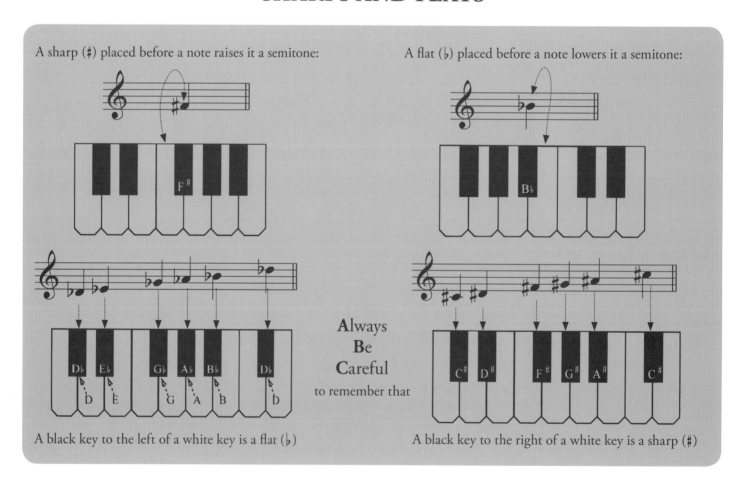

NATURAL

A natural (♮) placed before a note which has been either sharpened or flattened cancels the sharp or flat.

WHOLE TONES

A whole tone is twice the distance of a semitone.

Therefore, there will always be one key – either black or white – lying between.

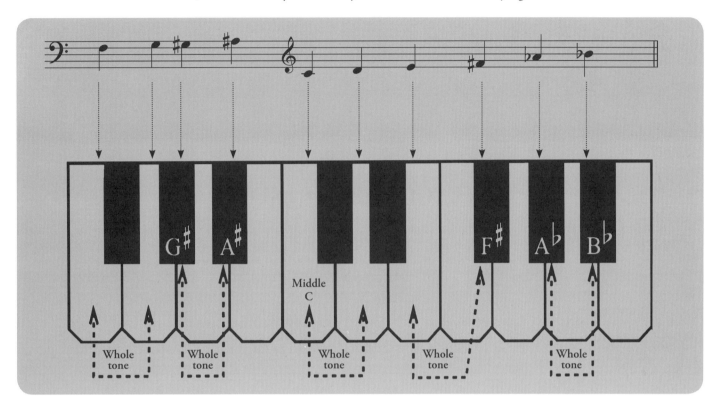

IDENTIFYING WHOLE TONES AND SEMITONES

Describe the following examples in terms of whole tones and semitones.

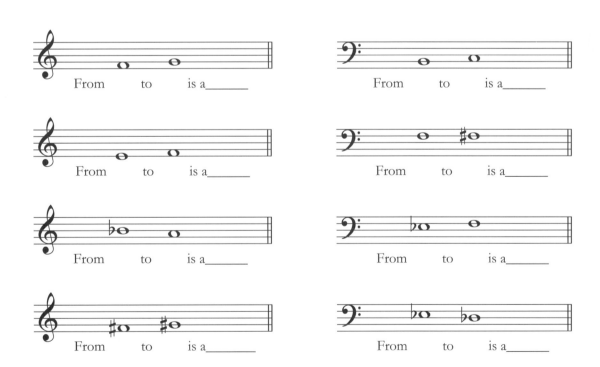

From _____ to _____ is a _____

From _____ to _____ is a _____

From _____ to _____ is a _____

From _____ to _____ is a _____

From _____ to _____ is a _____

From _____ to _____ is a _____

From _____ to _____ is a _____

From _____ to _____ is a _____

ACCIDENTALS

THE SCISSORS GRINDER

Moderato ♩ = 60–162

Track No. 6

Round   and   round,   round   and   round

mp

Goes   the   wheel   when   scis - sors   are   ground. The

edge   is   sharp   that   was   flat!

p

Scis - sors   grind - ers   'tend   to   that.

Or up to ♩. = 54.

Play with as much expression as possible:
and note the new expression signs:

means *crescendo*, a gradual increase in volume.

means *decrescendo*, a gradual decrease in volume.

NEW HAND POSITION – G MAJOR

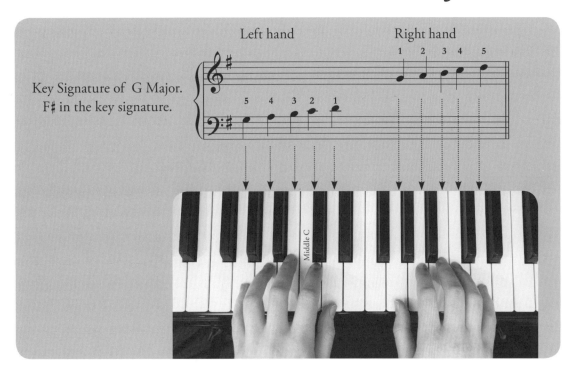

Key Signature of G Major.
F♯ in the key signature.

Left hand   Right hand

We change now to a new key – the key of G Major – and consequently to a new hand position. Note the sharp (♯) in the key signature. This means that all Fs will be sharpened (played on a black key). Be sure to remember this. Place your hands in the new hand position and practise each hand separately before you play the piece.

A SONG OF PENNY CANDY

Track No. 7

♩ = 60–120

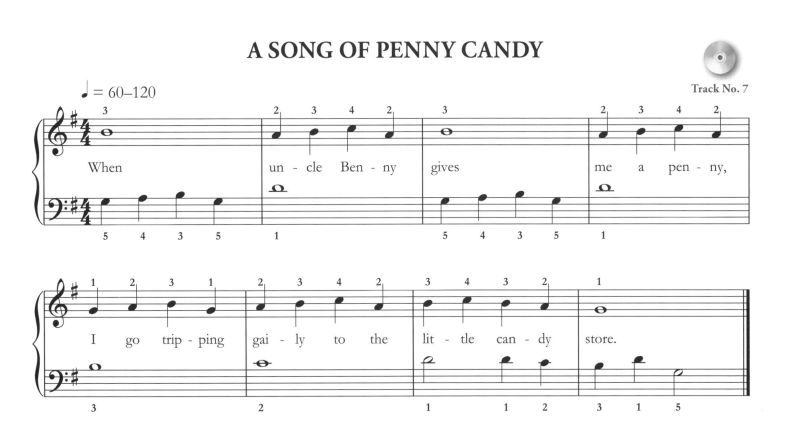

When un-cle Ben-ny gives me a pen-ny,

I go trip-ping gai-ly to the lit-tle can-dy store.

Note to Teachers: Students should be required to recite both time signature and key signature before playing each piece.

13

TWO MELODY PATTERNS

Notice the form of this little piece. The entire theme is written on two melody patterns.

THE MAN IN THE MOON

Track No. 8

Or up to ♩ = 54.

Andante means at a walking pace.

TRANSPOSITION: By means of finger patterns the pupil should now be taught to transpose the C Major pieces into the key of G Major and vice versa. Simply find the five-finger position for the new key and play with the same fingers as in the original key. This idea should be carried on in each new key as learned.

FOLK TUNES

Some of our most beautiful melodies did not, as you might suppose, come from the pen of famous composers, but from the folk songs which originated among everyday communities. These melodies were not written down, but were passed along orally from generation to generation. Because of their charming simplicity, many of them will endure forever as masterpieces of melody. Note this beautiful old French folk tune which consists of two very short melody patterns.

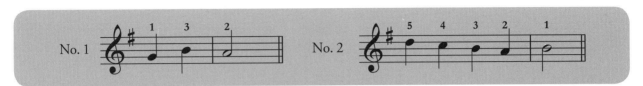

THE PARTY

Track No. 9

Andante ♩ = 60–120

COUNT: THREE four **ONE** two THREE four

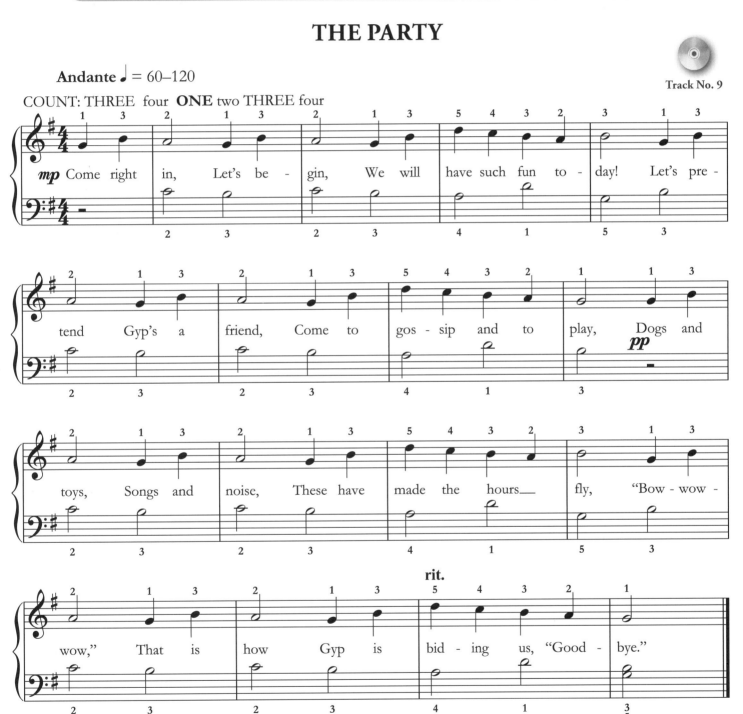

MELODIES BEGINNING ON THE VARIOUS BEATS OF THE BAR

Melodies do not always begin on the first beat of the bar. This piece, for instance, begins on the third beat, adding an entirely new 'swing' to the rhythm. To produce this effect we must be careful to apply the accent where it belongs – on the first beat.
COUNT therefore: | THREE four | **ONE** two THREE four | **ONE** two THREE four | etc.

PHRASING ATTACK

Phrasing in music is like breathing in speech – we take short breaths and long breaths. If we keep in mind to make our playing breathe at the end of each phrase, it will strengthen the rhythm and add immensely to the interpretation.

In playing two-note phrases, think of the words 'drop, roll' and the effect will come naturally. In the following example, play the first note with a gentle drop of the arm and the second note with a roll of the arm and hand in an inward and upward motion, using no finger action, and releasing the note on the upward roll. The following illustration shows the proper position of hand and arm as each phrase is released. The wrist must be completely relaxed.

Play the following with the right hand:

Play the following with the left hand:

The sign of the phrase is the curved line, ⌒ . All notes under this line, except the last one, should be played *legato*. The last note must always be played with a rolling motion of the arm forward and upward.

At this stage of progress the *Hanon Preliminary Studies* by John Thompson (WMR000352) should be assigned as supplementary work. This book is especially adapted for beginner use to develop the phrasing attack, as well as all the fundamental touches covered in this book.

COMBINING HAND POSITIONS

To play this piece we combine the hand positions learned in C Major and G Major. The right hand plays the five-finger position beginning on C while the left hand plays the five-finger position beginning on G.

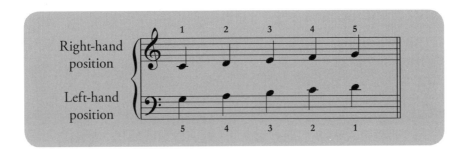

Practise with the hands in this position then play 'The Robin'.

THE ROBIN

Track No. 10

Or up to ♩ = 60.

Be sure to phrase the right hand as indicated by the curved lines using the drop, roll attack.

COUNT: three | **ONE** two three | **ONE** two three | etc.

FINGER AND HARMONY PATTERNS

Have you noticed how easy it is to transpose from one key to another by means of the five-finger pattern?
A knowledge of finger patterns is also very helpful when playing beyond the five-finger position.

In playing 'The Merry Clown', the left hand goes out of the five-finger position, but observe how easily the left hand trips down the keyboard on a simple little 'one-two' finger pattern.

The right-hand harmony pattern is also extremely simple, consisting of but two small chords.

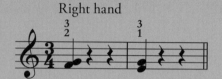

Practise each pattern separately before playing hands together.

THE MERRY CLOWN

Track No. 11

♩ = 80+

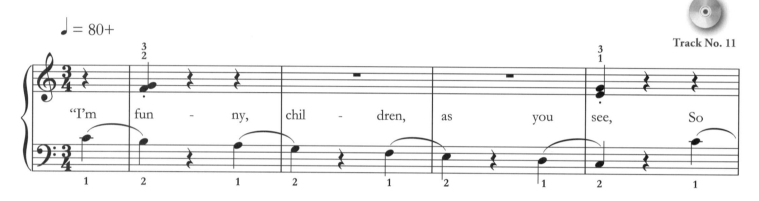

"I'm fun - ny, chil - dren, as you see, So

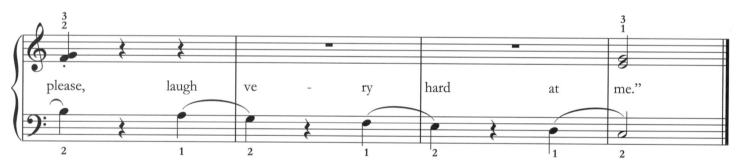

please, laugh ve - ry hard at me."

Be sure to observe the left-hand phrasing by use of the drop, roll attack.

Round dots (•) over or under notes indicate *staccato* – detached – short.

Always **B**e **C**areful of the accent. The melody begins on the third beat.

COUNT: three | **ONE** two three | **ONE** two three | etc.

18

Historically, nearly every phase of life in Germany was bound together in the national tie of folk songs – songs which reflected the moral, social and political aspects of all walks of life. When Europeans settled in America, they took these beautiful melodies with them. Later generations of settlers forgot the words of the songs but not the tunes, adapting them and absorbing them into their own traditions.

In 'The Cuckoo', both hands employ the phrasing attack. Place your hands in the G Major five-finger position and be sure you are familiar with the harmony pattern in the left hand.

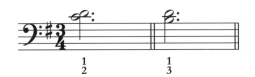

THE CUCKOO

German Folk Tune

Or up to ♩ = 50.

ff = *fortissimo*. Very loud.

EXAMINATION NO. 1

1. Explain the following time signatures and say where the accents fall in each.

....

2. What is a semitone?............................ A whole tone?..

3. Give the definition of the following:

   Moderato..

   Legato ....

   Andante..

   Ritardando..

   Tempo ....

4. Write the meaning and signs of the following musical terms.

   Forte .... Its sign ....

   Mezzo forte.. Its sign ....

   Piano.. Its sign ....

   Mezzo piano.. Its sign ....

   Pianissimo .... Its sign ....

   Fortissimo.. Its sign ....

5. What are accidentals and what effect do they have?..

6. What are folk tunes?..

AVERAGE GRADE for Examination No. 1: ....

Attach Certificate No. 1 here

Note to teacher: Students may be graded according to the preference of the individual teacher. Some teachers prefer the use of silver and gold stars; some grade by percentage, while others find the letter system of grading as used in schools more adaptable.

When the above examination has been passed to the satisfaction of the teacher, the student should be awarded Certificate No. 1 (See page 79 of this book) duly signed, dated and graded.

SCALES

The matter of scales and arpeggios practice is a much debated question among piano teachers. Some teachers begin scale work quite early in the student's career and are very insistent in the matter of daily practice. Others look upon them as a sort of unnecessary drudgery and claim that students can develop just as much facility in playing the scale and arpeggio passages that occur in the books and sheet music of their repertoire. Naturally, this resolves itself into a matter of individual judgement.

The author feels that since all music is made up of scales and arpeggio figures, or fragments thereof, pupils should be required to know something about them. All music has form and shape that should be recognised in order to aid interpretation and general musicianship. There is also a technical value to scale and arpeggio practice which cannot be summarily dismissed. Perhaps the real difficulty arises from the theory that most students look upon the scale as a dry, uninteresting exercise invented by the teacher as a special form of punishment. If more care were used in presenting the scale and a real effort made to have the student look upon the scale as a beautiful piece of musical architecture, the result would be quite different. As soon as the formation of a scale is learned, students should be assigned pieces in which the scale figure is employed as melody. In this way the student learns to greet the scale as an interesting musical pattern and one which will recur many times, even in elementary repertoire.

There are many ways to teach the scales, but most of the variations are based upon two standard approaches. Some teachers prefer the 'tetrachord' approach while others find the older formula (i.e. the semitones between the third and fourth and the seventh and eighth) more acceptable. Of course, this is a matter that will vary not only with teachers, but also with students. This book has been arranged so that either approach may be made, at the discretion of the teacher.

The Technical Drills on pages 76–78 of this book contain exercises for the development of scales and arpeggios.

THE MAJOR SCALE

BUILDING THE C MAJOR AND G MAJOR SCALES

A scale is a succession of eight notes bearing letter names in alphabetical order, the last note having the same letter name as the first. The figures 1, 2, 3, 4, 5, 6, 7, 8 are called the degrees of the scale.

A major scale is a succession of whole tones and semitones.
The semitones occur between 3 and 4 and between 7 and 8 as follows:

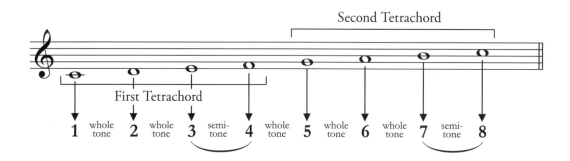

The above chart shows how a major scale is composed of two tetrachords, each tetrachord separated by a whole tone. Play the scale of C Major as follows, using the fingers indicated.

SCALE OF G MAJOR

Note to Teachers: During the progress in this book, it is advisable to adhere to the above form – the scale divided between the hands – until scale construction in all keys has been thoroughly mastered. This obviates the necessity of passing the thumb under and the hand over – a procedure which is comprehensively taken up and illustrated by examples in the second grade book.

SCALE OF C MAJOR – ASCENDING

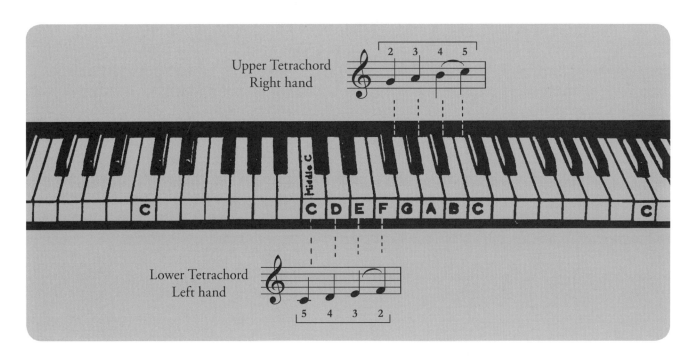

Upper Tetrachord
Right hand

Lower Tetrachord
Left hand

SCALING THE WALL

Track No. 13

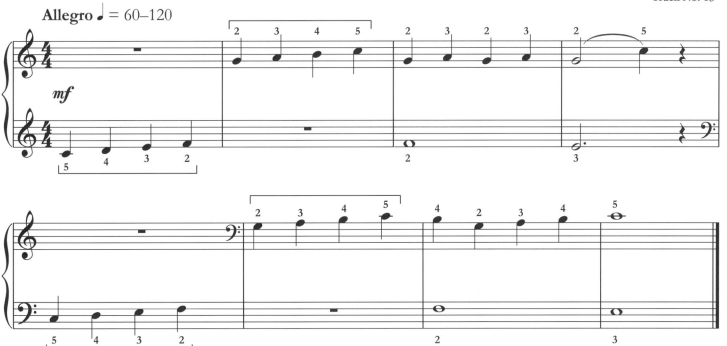

Allegro means quickly.

Note to Teachers: This is an excellent exercise for use in the various keys as they are learned. It should be played finally in all of the major keys.

SCALE OF C MAJOR – DESCENDING

THE CHIMES

THE PEDAL

No doubt, your teacher has told you not to use the pedal. This has been done for an excellent reason, which you will appreciate when you have advanced a little further.

But perhaps as a reward for obedience in this matter, your teacher may, upon request, allow you to use the pedal just once in order to make the chimes sound like real church chimes.

If permission is given, hold down the pedal from beginning to end. The result will be a blur which will be very unpleasant in most pieces – and that is one of the reasons your teacher does not want you to use the pedal yet. But in this particular tune it will give a clangorous muddle, typical of church chimes, filling the air with overtones.

NEW HAND POSITION – FOR THE LEFT HAND

STEPPING STONES

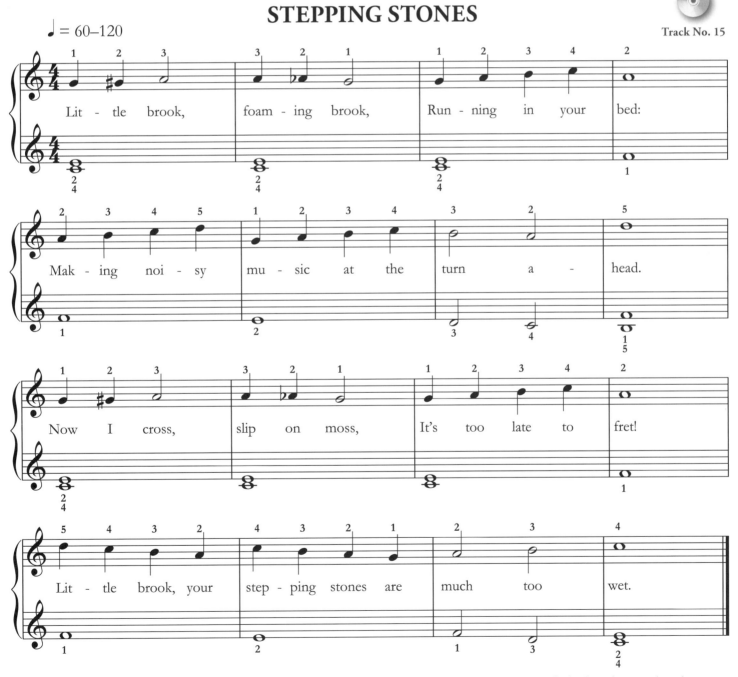

Track No. 15

SEMITONES: The melody in the right hand of stepping stones passes through 16 semitones, of which eight are white-key semitones. Can you locate all of them?

CHORD BUILDING

A chord is a group of three or more notes. The note on which a chord is built is called the root.

INTERVALS

An interval is the difference in pitch between two tones.
Intervals are measured by the number of letter names contained between the lower and upper notes inclusively.

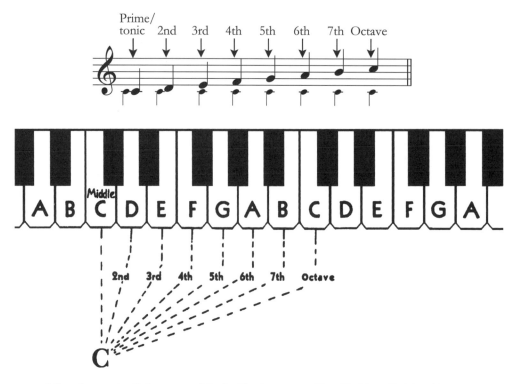

All scales are built in steps of 2nds. For instance: C to D, D to E, E to F etc.

TRIADS

A triad is a chord of three tones built in steps of 3rds, and contains a root, a 3rd and a 5th. For instance: C to E, E to G.

EVERY CHORD IS NAMED FOR ITS ROOT

See Technical Drills on pages 77–78 for broken chord practice.

CHORD INVERSIONS

We have learned that a triad contains a root, a 3rd and a 5th.

The order of these notes may change without changing the name of the chord.

When the lowest note is the root, the triad is in root position.
When the lowest note is not the root, the triad is said to be inverted.

C MAJOR TRIAD

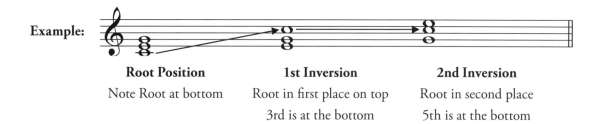

Root Position	**1st Inversion**	**2nd Inversion**
Note Root at bottom	Root in first place on top	Root in second place
	3rd is at the bottom	5th is at the bottom

SIMPLE RULES FOR RECOGNISING INVERTED CHORDS

Triads are in root position when all the intervals of the chord look alike;
that is, when the notes are either all on the lines or all in the spaces.

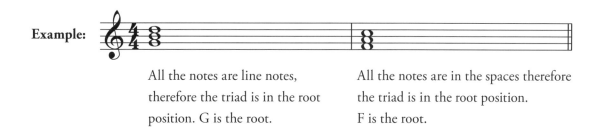

All the notes are line notes, therefore the triad is in the root position. G is the root.

All the notes are in the spaces therefore the triad is in the root position. F is the root.

When triads are inverted the intervals of the chord are unlike and appear mixed, that is, some of the notes are on the lines and some are in spaces.

C MAJOR TRIAD

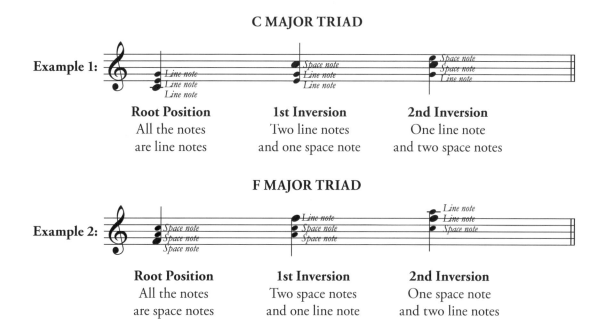

Root Position	**1st Inversion**	**2nd Inversion**
All the notes are line notes	Two line notes and one space note	One line note and two space notes

F MAJOR TRIAD

Root Position	**1st Inversion**	**2nd Inversion**
All the notes are space notes	Two space notes and one line note	One space note and two line notes

The root is always the first note (counting upwards) to change its position from space to line or from line to space.

BROKEN CHORD AS A MELODY

In 'Mountain Climbing' note how the broken chord is used as the melody. In the first two bars it is marked with a dotted circle. Locate the other broken chords and enclose each of them with a circle.

C MAJOR HAND POSITION

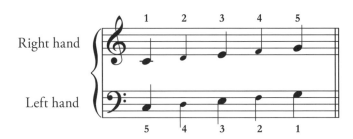

MOUNTAIN CLIMBING

Track No. 16

Or up to $\downarrow = 50$.

NEW HAND POSITION – F MAJOR

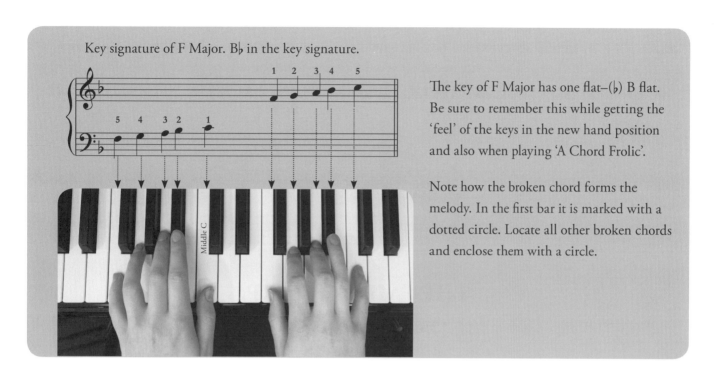

Key signature of F Major. B♭ in the key signature.

The key of F Major has one flat–(♭) B flat. Be sure to remember this while getting the 'feel' of the keys in the new hand position and also when playing 'A Chord Frolic'.

Note how the broken chord forms the melody. In the first bar it is marked with a dotted circle. Locate all other broken chords and enclose them with a circle.

A CHORD FROLIC

Track No. 17

Or up to ♩ = 50.

FIRST RECITAL PIECE

Here is your first real recital piece! See if you can learn it well enough to play on the next performance opportunity presented by your teacher. Remember all the points you have learned thus far about rhythm, tone colouring, expression, broken chords, etc., and apply your knowledge to this piece.

A wavy line preceding a chord means that the notes of the chord are to be broken instead of sounded together.

THE FAIRIES' HARP

A fairy harp hangs in the wood
Played by every breeze,
Vanished today are the fairy folk
Who hung it high in the trees.

Or up to ♩ = 50.

INTRODUCTION TO QUAVERS

Note to Teachers: Frequently, we hear differences of opinion over the question of allowing students to say 'and' when counting quavers. As with all other controversial subjects in music, it is ridiculous to say that, 'This and this only is the correct way to teach'. The progressive teacher applies his or her own individuality to the respective characteristic of each student. Whatever may prove successful with one may fail utterly with another. Experiment with all the approaches you know and use the one which justifies itself. It is often easier for a student to grasp the idea that there are two quavers to one count rather than 'a quaver gets half a count'. Small children know nothing about fractions. Perhaps the simplest way is to play a few quavers for the student and allow the ear to catch the rhythmical inflexion rather than try to appeal to the student's mathematical faculties at this stage.

TWO HAND POSITIONS IN THE KEY OF C MAJOR

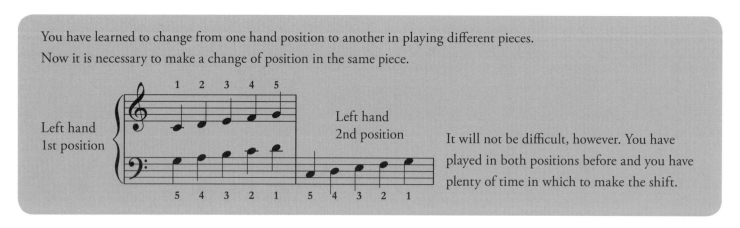

You have learned to change from one hand position to another in playing different pieces.
Now it is necessary to make a change of position in the same piece.

Left hand 1st position

Left hand 2nd position

It will not be difficult, however. You have played in both positions before and you have plenty of time in which to make the shift.

THE WISHING STAR

Track No. 19

German Folk Tune

♩ = 60–108

Or up to ♩ = 54.

32

NEW HAND POSITION – D MAJOR

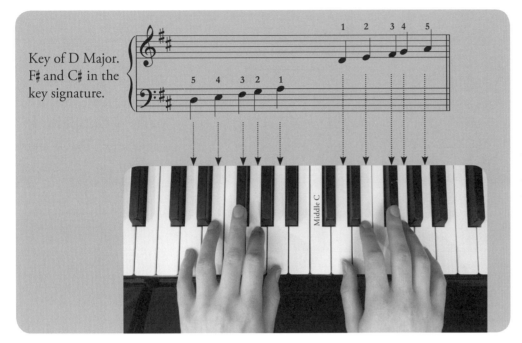

Key of D Major.
F♯ and C♯ in the
key signature.

See how nicely you can phrase 'Lightly Row' by using the drop and roll attack on the two-note phrases. On the extended phrases drop on the first note, connect all notes in between, and roll off on the last note.

LIGHTLY ROW

Track No. 20

Moderato

Light - ly row! light - ly row! O'er the glass - y waves we go;

Smooth - ly glide! smooth - ly glide! On the si - lent tide.

Let the winds and wa - ters be Min - gled with our me - lo - dy;

Sing and float! sing and float! In our lit - tle boat.

NEW HAND POSITION – A MAJOR

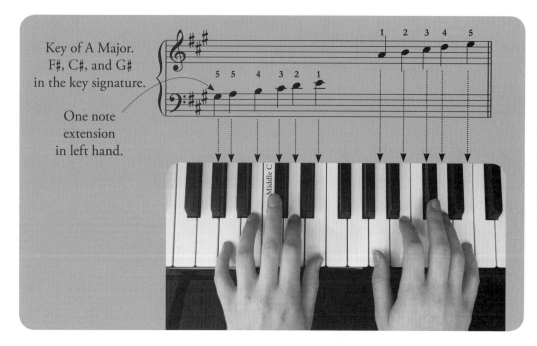

Key of A Major. F♯, C♯, and G♯ in the key signature.

One note extension in left hand.

The key of A Major has three sharps – F♯, C♯ and G♯. Here again we have a recital piece. This calls for a smooth and beautiful singing tone.

LITTLE SPRING SONG

Track No. 21

Andantino ♩ = 60–150

Lit - tle breeze from the South
You can sing tho' you have no mouth.
Lit - tle songs, young and gay,
Full of cheer as a sum - mer day.

Or up to ♩ = 50.

STACCATO AND *LEGATO* GROUPS

Make as much contrast as possible between the *staccato* notes and the *legato* groups in this piece.
Also see how much tonal shading you can put into it. Note the decided shading from ***ff*** to ***pp*** in the
last line. Lay special emphasis on the notes marked with the accent sign thus: $\overset{>}{\rho}$

FALLING LEAVES

Dry leaves float down with every gust
Because old Autumn says they must!

Track No. 22

DANCE FORMS

In music, rhythm is always uppermost. This is particularly true when playing dance forms. It is the rhythm that gives the dance its distinctive character. In a 'Dutch Dance' the accent is a very heavy one. The first beat is usually phrased into the second and shaped off sharply. Imagine Dutch children dancing in their wooden shoes and see if you can make this piece suggest the land of canals, dykes and tulips.

DUTCH DANCE

Track No. 23

Or up to ♩ = 56.

A DESCRIPTIVE RECITAL PIECE

This recital piece can be easily learned if studied in the following manner:

First – Analyse the introduction which consists of the F Major chord, built up note by note as each new trumpeter joins the Fanfare.

Next – Examine the left-hand harmony pattern which is very simple, consisting of only two chords.

Practise them in this manner until you can make the shift easily.

Play the left-hand chords with wrist *staccato*, using a snappy, bouncing wrist. Next apply the right hand, making a nice contrast between *staccato* and *legato*. Keep the tempo in a strict march time and play with military precision. Note the F Major scale divided between the hands in bar 11.

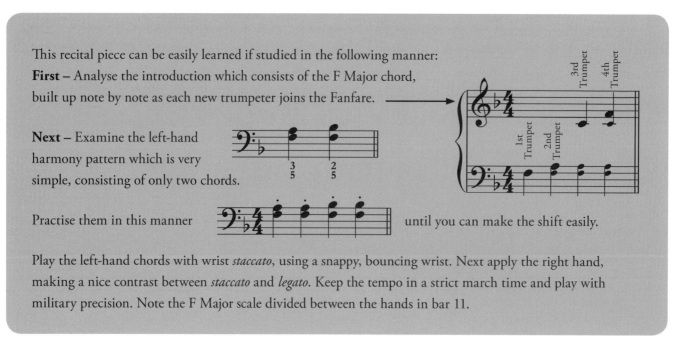

THE FAIRY COURT

Track No. 24

⌢ = pause. Hold.

EXAMINATION NO. 2

1. What is the major scale composed of? ....

2. What degrees of the scale are used in building the major triad? ....

3. What are inversions? ....

    How many inversions has the triad? ....

4. What is the value of a quaver? ....

    Grade on above oral examination ....

5. Play the following scales, first reciting the key signature of each.

    Grade

    C Major ....

    G Major ....

    F Major ....

    D Major ....

    A Major ....

    Average grade for scale playing ....

6. Play the following triads in root position, 1st inversion and 2nd inversion, naming each position.

    Grade

    C Major ....

    G Major ....

    F Major ....

    D Major ....

    A Major ....

    Average grade for triad playing ....

    AVERAGE GRADE for Examination No. 2: ....

    Attach Certificate No. 2 here

    (See page 79)

EXAMPLE IN *STACCATO*

Play this number with a 'pecking' sort of wrist *staccato*. The wrist should bounce freely and easily, but at the same time crisply.

THE TIRESOME WOODPECKER

The Woodpecker is a bird
That makes me exceedingly tired!
To go tapping like that for my food
I simply couldn't be hired!

Track No. 25

Note to Teachers: For further development of wrist staccato use the *Hanon Preliminary Studies* by John Thompson.

EXTENDED HAND POSITION – A MAJOR

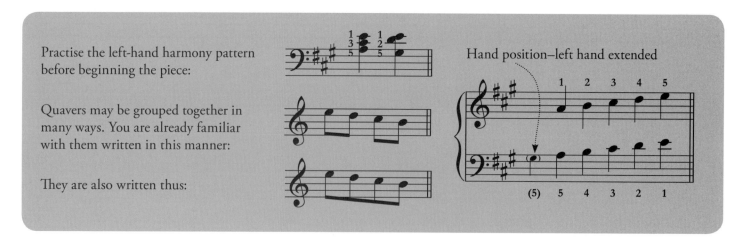

Practise the left-hand harmony pattern before beginning the piece:

Quavers may be grouped together in many ways. You are already familiar with them written in this manner:

They are also written thus:

Hand position–left hand extended

THE KNIGHT AND THE LADY

Riding through the green and leafy wood
Comes a lady wearing cloak and hood,
She is very sad,
Isn't that too bad?
Surely we would help her if we could!

Lo! A gallant knight comes riding by,
How he hates to see a lady cry!
He will take her part,
Win her gentle heart,
Quietly we'll leave them, you and I.

Track No. 26

DOTTED CROTCHETS

You have already played dotted minims and learned how the dot set after a note increases the time of that note by half its value. Therefore, if a crotchet is equal to one count, a dotted crotchet will naturally be equal to one count and a half, or one full beat and half of the next one.

Introduction of the dotted crotchet adds a new rhythmical pattern to those already learned.

By reciting the word 'Cumberland' you will get the 'feel' of the dotted crotchet. Before playing this piece practise this exercise and the new hand position.

Practise each hand separately

CUM - ber - land, CUM - ber - land, CUM - ber - land.

'AIR' BY MOZART

Track No. 27

Mozart was one of the most musical boys that ever lived. He was born in the little town of Salzburg, in Austria, on January 27, 1756. At the age of four his father gave him his first music lesson; when he was six years old he composed a little minuet and while still a child played at court for King Francis I and Queen Maria Theresa of Austria.

RHYTHMICAL PATTERN – USED BY BRAHMS

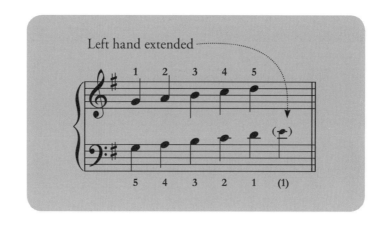

A LITTLE WALTZ

Track No. 28

This piece follows almost the exact rhythmical pattern used by Brahms in one of his most famous waltzes.

NEW HAND POSITION — B♭ MAJOR

A nocturne is a Night Song. It is a composition written in lyric style suggesting the peace of evening.

This one is written in the key of B♭ Major. The melody in the right hand should be played with a smooth singing tone. Make the phrases 'breathe' on the 2nd and 4th lines. Play the left hand with a light touch so that the singing tone will predominate in the right hand.

THE OWL'S QUESTION

(Nocturne)

Track No. 29

⁶⁄₈ TIME

In ⁶⁄₈ time there are six counts to the bar and a quaver gets one count.

There are two accents to the bar, the primary accent falling on the first count
and a secondary accent on the fourth count.

A dotted crotchet, of course, gets three counts in ⁶⁄₈ time.

Note to Teachers: When students can play these ⁶⁄₈ examples up to tempo
they should be taught to count two to the bar.

CHEER FOR THE BLUE

Track No. 30

Brek - ek - ek, Brek - ek - ek, Brek - ek - ek - ek, Ray! Par - a - ba - loo!

Brek - ek - ek, Brek - ek - ek, Brek - ek - ek - ek, Yea, cheer for the blue!

TWO-NOTE PHRASES IN $\frac{6}{8}$ TIME

The rhythm in The 'Cuckoo Clock' begins on the sixth count.

Always **B**e **C**areful, therefore, to count as follows:

six | **ONE**, two, three, Four, five, six | etc.
Be sure to observe the two-note phrases of the right hand, using the drop and roll (phrasing) attack.

THE CUCKOO CLOCK

Track No. 31

$\frac{6}{8}$ TIME – G MAJOR

Hand position – key of G Major

THE SINGING MOUSE

I'm not an ordinary mouse,
I lend distinction to a house!
Who wouldn't like to see
A singing mouse like me?

EXTENDED HAND POSITION – F MAJOR

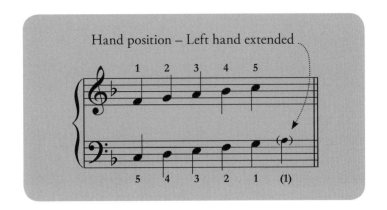

Hand position – Left hand extended

THE BIRTHDAY CAKE

No wonder the children to whom I come
Greet me with shouts and cheers,
I'm the glowing and beautiful birthday cake
That marks the passing years.

Track No. 33

D.S. (Dal Segno) al Fine means go back to the sign (𝄋) and play to *Fine*.

PLAYING IN TWO HAND POSITIONS

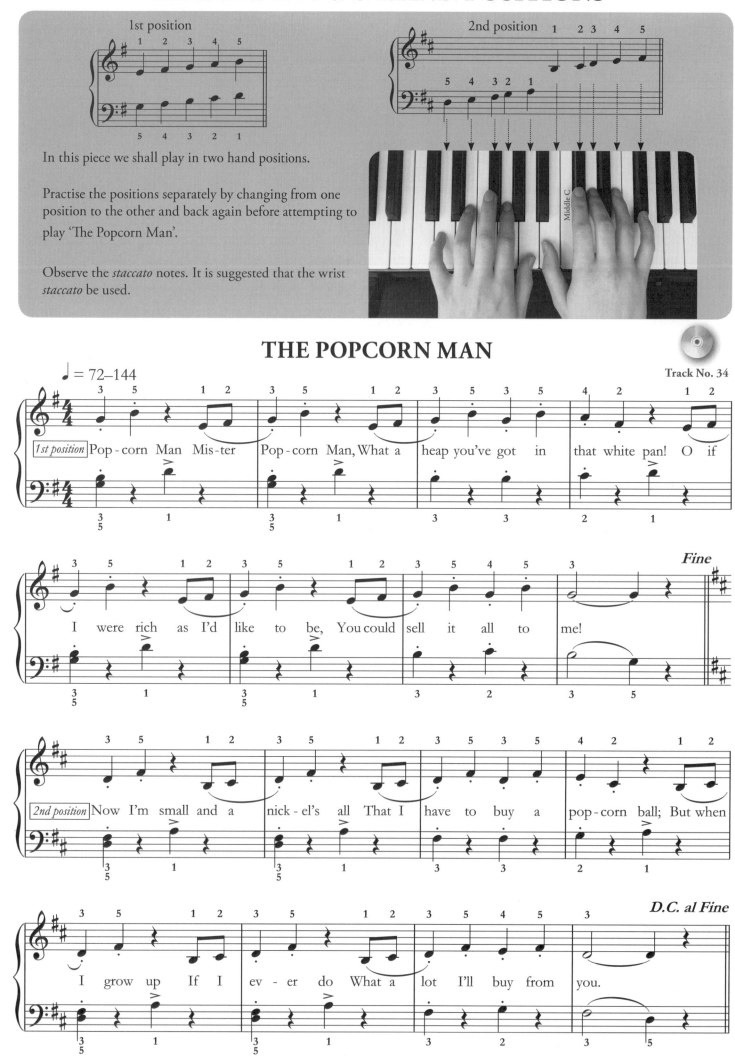

1st position

2nd position

In this piece we shall play in two hand positions.

Practise the positions separately by changing from one position to the other and back again before attempting to play 'The Popcorn Man'.

Observe the *staccato* notes. It is suggested that the wrist *staccato* be used.

THE POPCORN MAN

Track No. 34

♩ = 72–144

1st position Pop-corn Man Mis-ter Pop-corn Man, What a heap you've got in that white pan! O if

Fine

I were rich as I'd like to be, You could sell it all to me!

2nd position Now I'm small and a nick-el's all That I have to buy a pop-corn ball; But when

D.C. al Fine

I grow up If I ev-er do What a lot I'll buy from you.

50   *D.C. (Dal Capo) al fine* means return to the beginning and play to *Fine*.

TWO HAND POSITIONS – $\frac{6}{8}$ TIME

This piece requires two hand positions as shown here. Practise each pattern carefully. Accent each note bearing this sign ♩

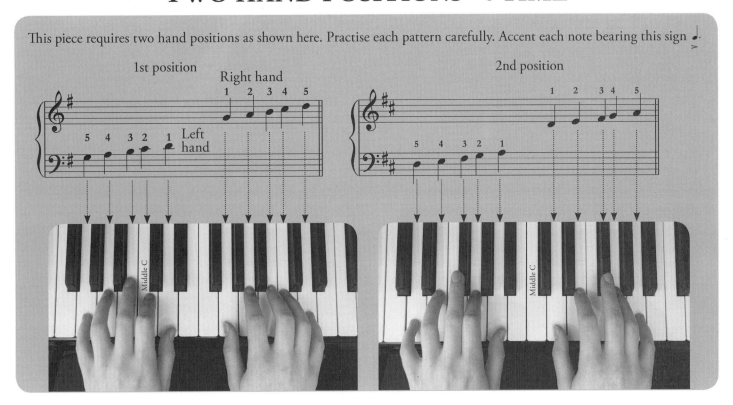

THE MERRY-GO-ROUND

I'm riding a kangaroo
When I'm not changing off to a gnu!
O, a merry-go-round is fun
For every age under the sun.

Track No. 35

SYNCOPATION

Here is another recital piece, this time with the atmosphere of Old Spain. *Fiesta*, the Spanish word for holiday, is a time of processions, dancing, feasting and merry-making.

The tying over of the last half of the first beat into the first half of the second beat results in a rhythmical effect known as syncopation. The effect will be distinguished by giving a slight emphasis to the notes marked ♩.

To learn this piece, first study the harmony pattern: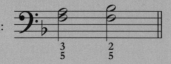

Then practise it in this form:

Now become familiar with the rhythmical pattern in the right hand. It is practically the same in every bar. Be sure to emphasise the notes marked ♩.

The student should be able to clap or tap the rhythm before attempting to play.
Follow all expression marks, play with good, sharp rhythm and earn a place on the next recital program.

A SPANISH FIESTA

In the street dance see them whirl;
Gallant boy and dark-eyed girl,
I would love to be in Spain
When Fiesta comes again!

Track No. 36

Note to Teachers: For additional practice rhythms, see the *Hanon Preliminary Studies* by John Thompson.

THE FOX HUNT

Play cheerfully and with vigour.

♩ = 50–108

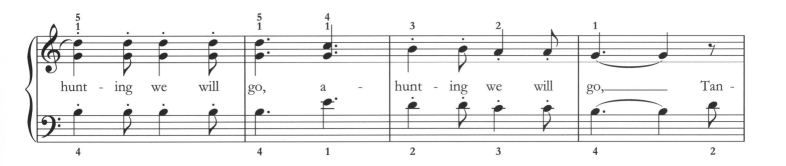

hunt - ing we will go, a - hunt - ing we will go,_____ Tan -

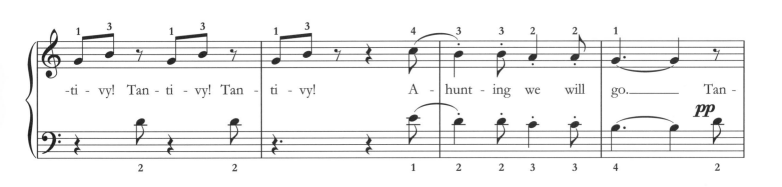

-ti - vy! Tan - ti - vy! Tan - ti - vy! A - hunt - ing we will go._____ Tan -

(Echo)

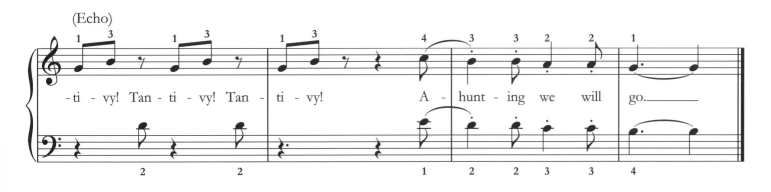

-ti - vy! Tan - ti - vy! Tan - ti - vy! A - hunt - ing we will go._____

TWO HAND POSITIONS – D MAJOR

Two hand positions in the right hand are required for this piece. Learn to play this familiar old song with feeling and it will prove a valuable addition to your repertoire.

First position   Second position

CELIA

Track No. 38

Andante ♪ = 72–138

with much expression

2nd position R.H.

1st position R.H.

Or up to ♩. = 46.

EXAMINATION NO. 3

1. What is the meaning of this sign, ⌢ ?...

2. What is syncopation?...........................

3. How much extra time is given to a dotted note?...

4. What should be uppermost when playing dance forms?.......................................

   Grade on above oral examination...........................

5. Play the following scales, first reciting the key signature of each.

   Grade

   A Major...............

   G Major..............

   B flat Major..........

   F Major..............

   Average grade for scale playing...............................

6. Play the following triads in root position, 1st inversion and 2nd inversion, naming each position.

   Grade

   A Major...............

   G Major..............

   B flat Major..........

   F Major..............

   Average grade for triad playing...............................

   AVERAGE GRADE for Examination No. 3: ....

Attach Certificate No. 3 here

(See page 79)

CROSS-HAND POSITION

Before attempting this piece, place your hands in the G Major position (first position, right) and bring your right hand over to the second position above. Practise until the movement becomes quite natural.

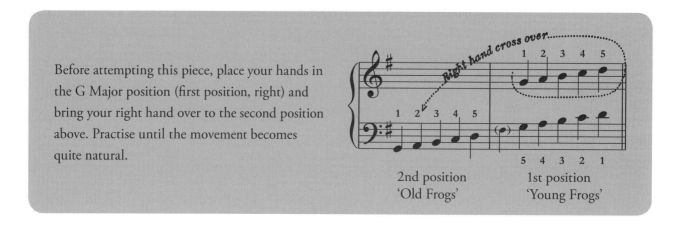

2nd position
'Old Frogs'

1st position
'Young Frogs'

THE FROG CHORUS

Over the lily pads
Froggies at play
Join in the chorus
To greet a new day.

Young frogs sing high
And the old frogs boom low,
All join the chorus
Their good will to show.

Track No. 39

58

WRIST *STACCATO*

Use a flexible, bouncing wrist when playing this piece and see how crisp you can make the *staccato* passages.

THE SLEIGH

Jingle, jingle, jingle,
In our sleigh we go,
Just like old Kris Kringle
Through the ice and snow.

Track No. 40

For students interested in keyboard harmony this example affords a splendid study in 2nds and 3rds.

Underline all 2nds. Draw circles around 3rds.

NEW HAND POSITION – E♭ MAJOR

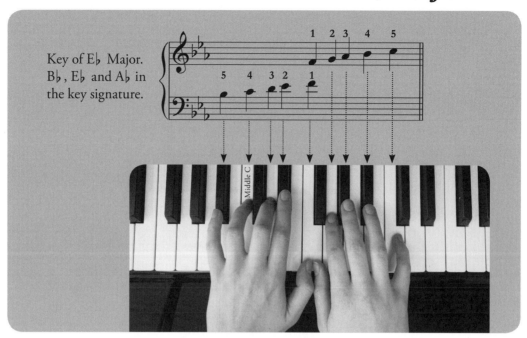

Key of E♭ Major.
B♭, E♭ and A♭ in
the key signature.

LITTLE BO-PEEP

Little Bo-Peep has lost her sheep
And looks for them sedately,
I wish she'd find them soon, because
We've had no lamb chops lately.

Track No. 41

Andante moderato ♩ = 66–150

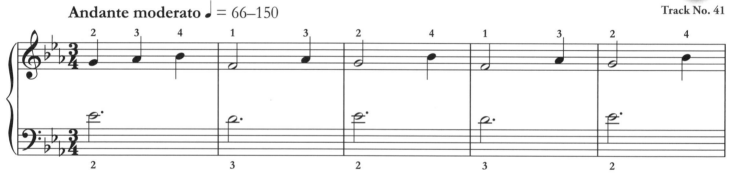

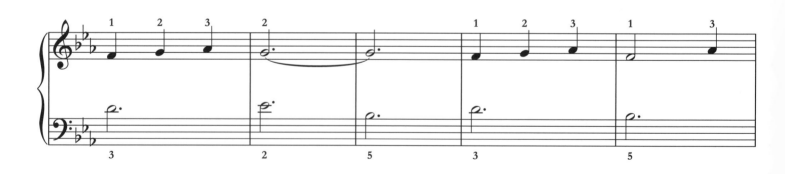

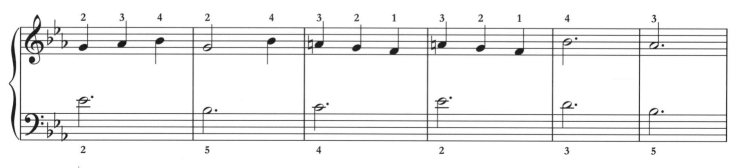

Or up to ♩ = 50.

61

THE FOREARM ATTACK

The forearm attack is used in playing large chords. Shape the chord with the hand, allowing the fingers to rest gently on the tops of the keys. Then press forward from the elbow (keeping the wrists loose) and the effect will be a sustained tone of good singing quality.

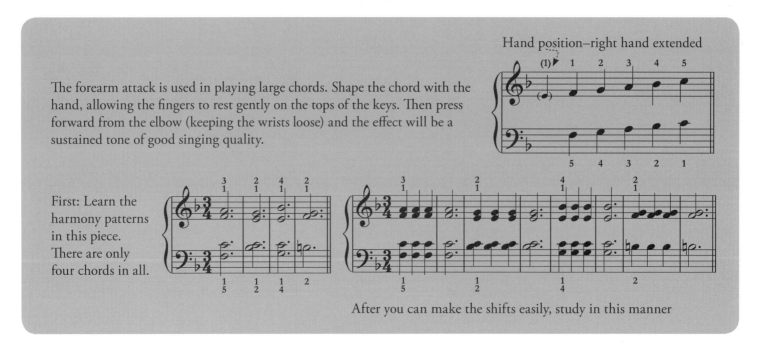

Hand position–right hand extended

First: Learn the harmony patterns in this piece. There are only four chords in all.

After you can make the shifts easily, study in this manner

EVENING BELLS

What say the bells
As the sun sinks down?
"Peace", they cry; "Peace
To Country and Town."

Track No. 42

Andante ♩ = 60–96

Note to Teachers: For further development of the forearm attack, see the *Hanon Preliminary Studies* by John Thompson.

NEW HAND POSITION – E MAJOR

Key of E Major.
F♯, C♯, G♯ and D♯
in the key signature.

In 'Peasant Dance' the
left-hand part represents the
drone of the bass viols, which
were often used to make the
music to which the peasants
danced on the village green.

PEASANT DANCE

All 'round the Maypole
Gather today,
Crowning a queen
Of the beautiful May.

Track No. 43

Rhythmically ♩ = 72–120

BROKEN CHORD ACCOMPANIMENT

TWO HAND POSITIONS

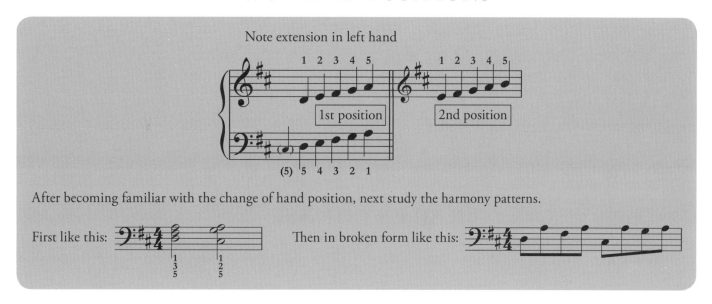

Note extension in left hand

1st position   2nd position

After becoming familiar with the change of hand position, next study the harmony patterns.

First like this: Then in broken form like this:

LONG, LONG AGO

Track No. 44

2nd position   *1st position* Thomas H. Bayly

Note to Teachers: the *Hanon Preliminary Studies* by John Thompson provides many useful examples in *legato* and *staccato*.

THREE HAND POSITIONS

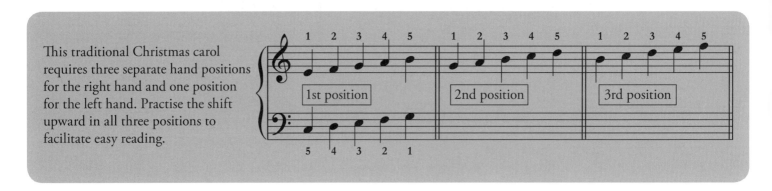

This traditional Christmas carol requires three separate hand positions for the right hand and one position for the left hand. Practise the shift upward in all three positions to facilitate easy reading.

SILENT NIGHT

Track No. 45

SCALE PATTERNS AND CHORDS
THREE HAND POSITIONS – FOR BOTH HANDS

Practise the scale patterns first as follows:

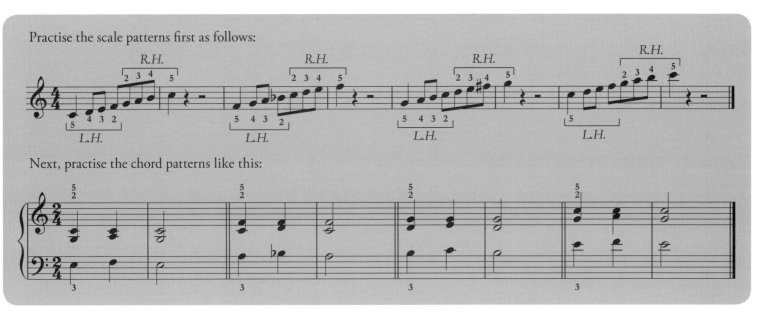

Next, practise the chord patterns like this:

A KEYBOARD RECREATION

If you think you can't have fun
With Scale and Chord,
Just play this little piece!
Now, were you bored?

Track No. 46

Allegro ♩ = 120

INTERPRETING CHARACTERISTIC MUSIC

Try to interpret this characteristic piece so that the friends for whom you play will enjoy the illusion.

CAUTION: Watch the expression marks!

THE STREAMLINER

Track No. 47

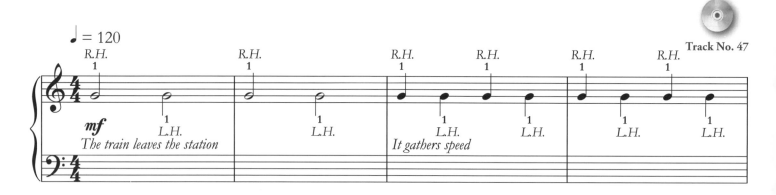

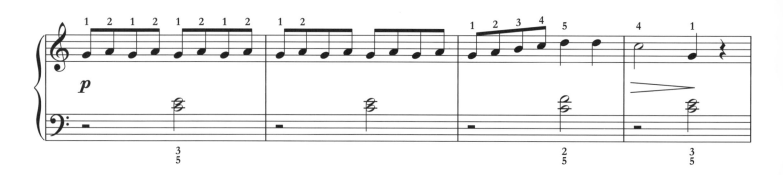

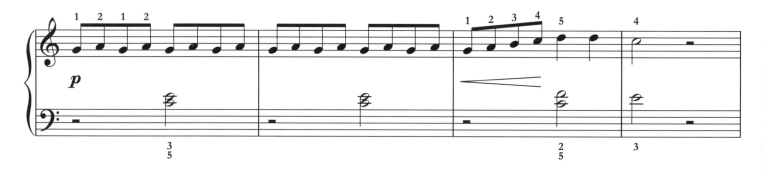

The whistle blows

and blows again

The train begins to slow down

Reaches journey's end.

NEW HAND POSITION – A♭ MAJOR

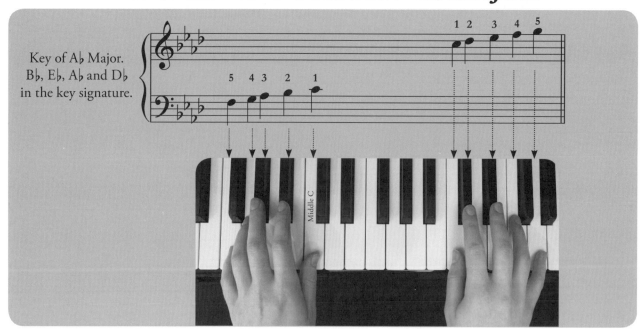

Key of A♭ Major.
B♭, E♭, A♭ and D♭
in the key signature.

TO A SKYSCRAPER

How very strong you must be made
Not to be a bit afraid!
How can you there amid the clouds
Look down so calmly on the crowds?

Track No. 48

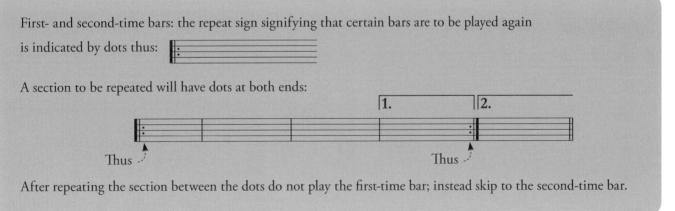

TWO HAND POSITIONS – FOR BOTH HANDS

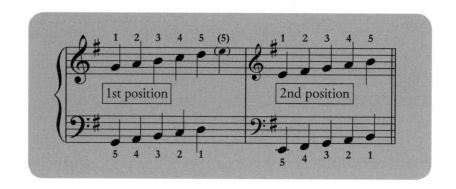

DUBLIN TOWN

I would be goin' to Dublin Town
If I had new shoes and a velvet gown,
But since I have neither, I drive my pigs
And fill my time gaily with songs and jigs.

Track No. 49

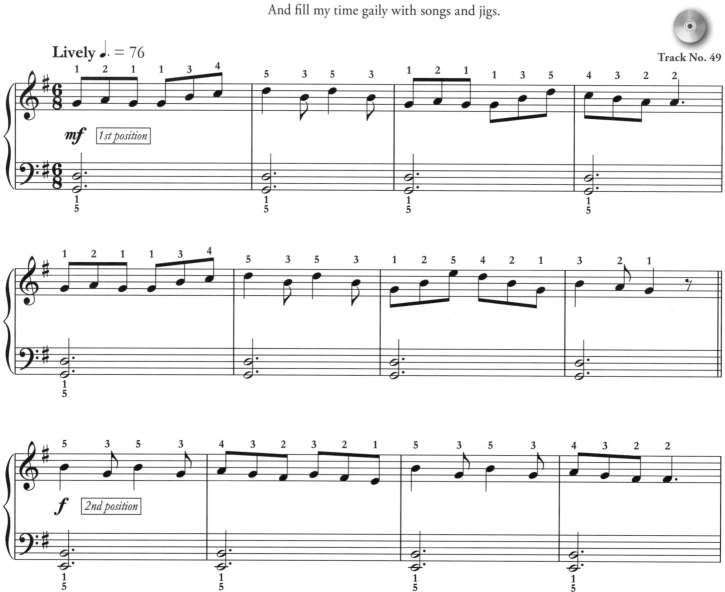

SEMIQUAVERS

The time value of semiquavers is half that of quavers. There are two semiquavers to one quaver:

and four semiquavers to one crotchet:

In this stirring piece your hands will be taken out of the five-finger position, but if you observe the finger patterns – 1, 2, 3 – 3, 2, 1 it will be quite easy to master.

JOHN PEEL

D'ye ken John Peel with his coat so gay?
D'ye ken John Peel at the break of day?
D'ye ken John Peel when he's far away
With his hounds and his horn in the morning?

Track No. 50

Scottish Folk Song

EXAMINATION NO. 4

1. What is a nocturne ?...

2. Explain $^6_8$ time..................................

3. What does *D.C. al Fine* mean?...

4. What is the value of a semiquaver?...

   Grade on above oral examination...........................

5. Play the following scales, first reciting the key signature of each.

   Grade

   E flat Major..........

   E Major..............

   D Major.............

   A flat Major..........

   Average grade for scale playing..............................

6. Play the following triads in root position, 1st inversion and 2nd inversion, naming each position.

   Grade

   E flat Major..........

   E Major..............

   D Major.............

   A flat Major..........

   Average grade for triad playing.............................

   AVERAGE GRADE for Examination No. 4: ....

   Attach Certificate No. 4 here

   (See page 79)

TECHNICAL DRILLS

Note to Teachers: Appended herewith are 16 technical exercises for the development of fingers, arms and wrists, including some drills in two-note and three-note phrasing attack. They are intended for use during the study of this book. They may be assigned purely at the option of the teacher, who will be governed, naturally, by the capacity of the student. If used, they should be taught by rote. The teacher should play each one slowly as it is assigned and allow the student to learn the finger and rhythmical patterns, thus making it possible to transpose into any key. These drills will do much to facilitate keyboard mastery if given a little practice daily. First, each hand separately – then together, an octave apart.

TWO-FINGER GROUPS–THE TRILL

THREE-FINGER GROUPS

FOUR-FINGER GROUPS

FIVE-FINGER GROUPS

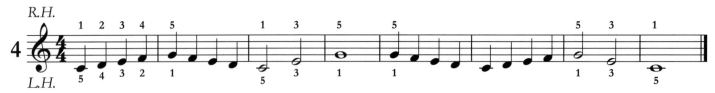

TWO-NOTE PHRASES
DROP-ROLL

THREE-NOTE PHRASES
DROP-CONNECT-ROLL

THE MAJOR SCALE DIVIDED BETWEEN THE HANDS

LEGATO EXERCISE

THE MAJOR SCALE WITH CADENCE CHORDS

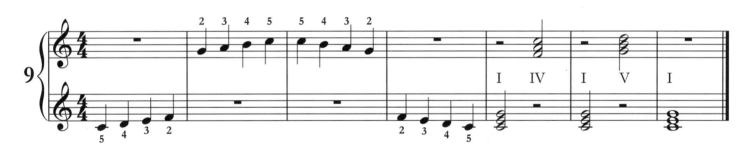

BROKEN CHORD – EXTENDED

BROKEN CHORD WITH INVERSIONS

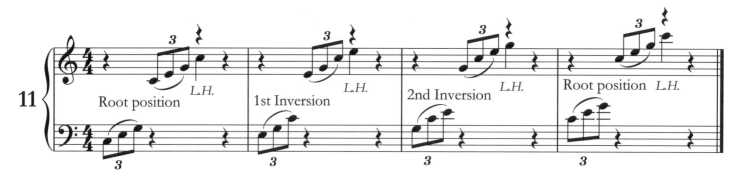

BROKEN CHORD AND DIATONIC FIGURES COMBINED

ASCENDING FINGER PATTERNS

FOREARM STROKE

WRIST STACCATO

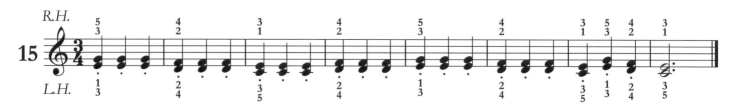

BROKEN CHORD DRILL BUGLE CALL

Certificate of Merit

This certifies that

....

has successfully passed

EXAMINATION No. 1

The First Grade Book of
John Thompson's Modern Course for the Piano

Teacher .... Date ....

Certificate of Merit

This certifies that

....

has successfully passed

EXAMINATION No. 2

The First Grade Book of
John Thompson's Modern Course for the Piano

Teacher .... Date ....

Certificate of Merit

This certifies that

....

has successfully passed

EXAMINATION No. 3

The First Grade Book of
John Thompson's Modern Course for the Piano

Teacher .... Date ....

Certificate of Merit

This certifies that

....

has successfully passed

EXAMINATION No. 4

The First Grade Book of
John Thompson's Modern Course for the Piano

Teacher .... Date ....

Each certificate to be cut out and pasted on respective page when earned by student.

Certificate of Merit

This certifies that

. . . .

has successfully completed

'John Thompson's First Grade Book'

and is eligible for promotion to

'John Thompson's Second Grade Book'

Teacher . . . .

Date . . . .

JOHN THOMPSON (1889–1963)

Talented American pianist/composer John Thompson was born in Pennsylvania. At an early age he appeared as a concert pianist in all of the principal cities of America and Europe, where his brilliant playing received the highest praise. After concluding his triumphant concert career he headed music departments at conservatories in Philadelphia, Indianapolis and Kansas City. During these tenures he developed certain definite and original ideas about teaching, and in a short time became famous for his sincere efforts to interest young pupils in pianism. All of his books teach, in the simplest language possible, interpretation and expression. One ideal is 'to use in miniature the same attacks as those used by the concert artist.'

OTHER TITLES BY JOHN THOMPSON...

JOHN THOMPSON'S EASIEST PIANO COURSE

This course is designed to present the easiest possible approach to piano playing, complete with an amusing family of characters and illustrations to help emphasise the information being taught. Each book of the course contains its own writing exercises, sight-reading drills, review work and later, technical studies. Accompaniments for teacher or parent are supplied with most of the examples.

JOHN THOMPSON'S EASIEST PIANO COURSE 1 NEW EDITION WMR000176 BK/CD WMR101002

JOHN THOMPSON'S EASIEST PIANO COURSE 2 NEW EDITION WMR000187 BK/CD WMR101013

JOHN THOMPSON'S EASIEST PIANO COURSE 3 NEW EDITION WMR000231 BK/CD WMR101024

JOHN THOMPSON'S EASIEST PIANO COURSE 4 NEW EDITION WMR000242 BK/CD WMR101035

JOHN THOMPSON'S EASIEST PIANO COURSE FIRST BEATLES HITS WMR100859

This collection of Beatles hits is intended as supplementary material for those working through *John Thompson's Easiest Piano Course Parts 2* and *3*, taking the player up to *Part 4*. The pieces may also be used for sight-reading practice by more advanced students.

JOHN THOMPSON'S EASY PIANO COURSE MANUSCRIPT BOOK WMR101046

JOHN THOMPSON'S FIRST...

Graded to work alongside the *Easiest Piano Course*, these pieces are ideal for pupils reaching *Part Two* and upwards. They are invaluable for securing basic technique at the same time as developing musicality and enjoyment.

JOHN THOMPSON'S FIRST DUETS PIANO WMR000209

JOHN THOMPSON'S FIRST CHRISTMAS TUNES PIANO WMR000210

JOHN THOMPSON'S FIRST NURSERY RHYMES PIANO WMR000220

JOHN THOMPSON'S FIRST FOLK SONGS PIANO WMR000550

JOHN THOMPSON'S FIRST CLASSICS PIANO WMR000638

JOHN THOMPSON'S FIRST BLUES & BOOGIES PIANO WMR000660

JOHN THOMPSON'S BOOK OF CHRISTMAS CAROLS PV WMR100936

TEACHING LITTLE FINGERS TO PLAY (BK/CD) WMR100947

TEACHING LITTLE FINGERS TO PLAY MORE PIANO WMR000627

CD TRACK LISTING

Each track is split—hear both piano and accompaniment if the balance is centred,
and the accompaniment only if the balance control is to the left!